SPOTLIGHT ON POETRY

Classic Poems 1

Contents

Collected by Brian Moses and David Orme

COLLINS

Acknowledgements

Whilst every effort has been made to contact the
copyright-holders and to secure the necessary permission
to reprint these selections, this has not proved to be possible
in every case.

'The Elephant' by Hilaire Belloc, published by Random
House UK Ltd, reprinted by permission of The Peters
Fraser and Dunlop Group Limited on behalf of The Estate
of Hilaire Belloc; 'The Tickle Rhyme' by Ian Serraillier,
from *The Tale of the Monster Horse* published by OUP.
© 1950, Ian Serraillier. Reprinted by permission of Anne
Serraillier; 'Some One', by Walter de la Mare, reprinted by
permission of The Literary Trustees of Walter de la Mare,
and the Society of Authors as their representative.

Published by Collins Educational
An imprint of HarperCollins*Publishers*
77–85 Fulham Palace Road
Hammersmith
London W6 8JB

www.**Collins**Education.com
On-line support for schools and colleges

© HarperCollins*Publishers* 1999

First published 1999

Reprinted 2000

Reprinted 0 9 8 7 6 5 4 3

ISBN 0 00 310 330 7

Designed by Clare Truscott
Cover Design by Clare Truscott and Kate Roberts
Illustrations by Tim Archbold, Phillip Burrows, Louise
Drake Lee, John Lupton, Maureen Galvani, Emma Garner,
Melanie Mansfield, Katty McMurray, Holly Swain

Printed and bound in Hong Kong by Printing Express

Collins Educational would like to thank the following
teachers and consultants who contributed to the research of
this series:

Mrs J. Bibby (St Paul's C of E Primary); Jason Darley, Liz
Hooley (Jessop Primary School); Mrs M.G. Farnell (High
Meadow First School); Alison Lewis; Chris Lutrario; Lesley
Moores (Princess Royal Primary School); Sheila Stamp
(Castle Lower School); Sally Prendergrast (Brooke Hill
School); Jenny Ransome; Jill Walkinton; Sue Webb; Michael
Webster (Castle Lower School); Jill Wells (St Andrews CE
Primary School).

The Pancake

Mix a pancake,
Stir a pancake,
Pop it in the pan.

Fry the pancake,
Toss the pancake,
Catch it if you can.

Christina Rossetti

3

The Elephant

When people call this beast to mind,
They marvel more and more
At such a little tail behind
So LARGE a trunk before.

Hilaire Belloc

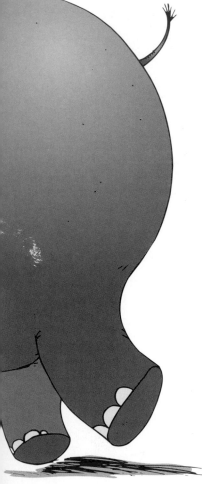

One Potato, Two Potato

One potato, two potato,
Three potato, four;
Five potato, six potato,
Seven potato, MORE.

Traditional

Betty Botter

Betty Botter bought some butter,
But, she said, the butter's bitter;
If I put it in my batter
It will make my batter bitter,
But a bit of better butter
Will make my batter better.
So she bought a bit of butter
Better than her bitter butter,
And she put it in her batter
And the batter was not bitter.
So t'was better Betty Botter
      bought a bit of better butter.

Traditional

She Sells Sea Shells

She sells sea shells
On the sea shore
And the sea shells she sells
Are sea shells I'm sure.

Traditional

The more you beg him to go home,
The more he dashes through the foam.

He rushes on, mile after mile,
And lands you on a desert isle.

And there, until some ship appears,
You often have to stay for years.

Lord Alfred Douglas

Solomon Grundy

Solomon Grundy,
Born on Monday,
Christened on Tuesday,
Married on Wednesday,
Took ill on Thursday,
Worse on Friday,
Died on Saturday,
Buried on Sunday.
This is the end
Of Solomon Grundy.

Traditional

10

Hurt No Living Thing

Hurt no living thing;
Ladybird, nor butterfly,
Nor moth with dusty wing,
Nor cricket chirping cheerily.
Nor grasshopper so light of leap,
Nor dancing gnat, nor beetle fat,
Nor harmless worms that creep.

Christina Rossetti

Bed in Summer

In winter I get up at night
And dress by yellow candle-light.
In summer, quite the other way,
I have to go to bed by day.

I have to go to bed and see
The birds still hopping on the tree,
Or hear the grown-up people's feet
Still going past me in the street.

And does it not seem hard to you,
When all the sky is clear and blue,
And I should like so much to play,
To have to go to bed by day?

R. L. Stevenson

Caterpillar

Brown and furry
Caterpillar in a hurry,
Take your walk
To the shady leaf, or stalk,

Or what not,
Which may be the chosen spot.
No toad spy you,
Hovering bird of prey pass by you;
Spin and die,
To live again a butterfly.

Christina Rossetti

Twinkle, Twinkle, Little Bat

Twinkle, twinkle, little bat!
How I wonder what you're at!
Up above the world you fly,
Like a tea-tray in the sky.

Lewis Carroll

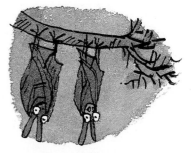

15

The Star

Twinkle, twinkle little star,
How I wonder what you are!
Up above the world so high,
Like a diamond in the sky.

When the blazing sun is gone,
When he nothing shines upon,
Then you show your little light,
Twinkle, twinkle, all the night.

Then the traveller in the dark,
Thanks you for your tiny spark,
He could not see which way to go,
If you did not twinkle so.

In the dark blue sky you keep,
And often through my curtains peep,
For you never shut your eye,
Till the sun is in the sky.

As your bright and tiny spark,
Lights the traveller in the dark–
Though I know not what you are,
Twinkle, twinkle, little star.

Jane Taylor

Some One

Some one came knocking
    At my wee, small door;
Some one came knocking,
    I'm sure – sure – sure;
I listened, I opened,
    I looked to left and right,
But nought there was a-stirring
    In the still dark night;

Only the busy beetle
   Tap-tapping in the wall,
Only from the forest
   The screech-owl's call,
Only the cricket whistling
   While the dewdrops fall,
So I know not who came knocking,
   At all, at all, at all.

Walter de la Mare

The Owl and the Pussy-Cat

I

The Owl and the Pussy-Cat went to sea
    In a beautiful pea-green boat,
They took some honey, and plenty of money,
    Wrapped up in a five-pound note.
The Owl looked up to the stars above,
    And sang to a small guitar,
"O lovely Pussy! O Pussy, my love,
    "What a beautiful Pussy you are,
        "You are,
        "You are!
    "What a beautiful Pussy you are!"

II

Pussy said to the Owl, "You elegant fowl!

"How charmingly sweet you sing!

"O let us be married! too long we have tarried:

"But what shall we do for a ring?"

They sailed away for a year and a day,

To the land where the Bong-Tree grows,

And there in a wood a Piggy-wig stood,

With a ring at the end of his nose,

His nose,

His nose,

With a ring at the end of his nose.

III

"Dear Pig, are you willing to sell for
one shilling
"Your ring?" Said the Piggy, "I will."
So they took it away, and were married
next day
By the Turkey who lives on the hill.
They dined on mince, and slices of quince,
Which they ate with a runcible spoon;
And hand in hand, on the edge of the sand,
They danced by the light of the moon,
The moon,
The moon,
They danced by the light of the moon.

Edward Lear

Glossary

Betty Botter
t'was   it was

The Whale
foam   the sea

Hurt No Living Thing
gnat   small, biting insect

Caterpillar
bird of prey   bird that kills other creatures for food

Some One
wee   tiny
nought   nothing
a-stirring   moving

The Owl and the Pussy-Cat
elegant fowl   beautiful bird
tarried   waited
Bong-Tree   an imaginary tree
shilling   coin in old money worth five pence
quince   fruit used for making jelly

runcible spoon   special spoon: part fork, part spoon.
The word 'runcible' was invented by Edward Lear for the
poem *The Owl and The Pussy-Cat*.

Index of poems by title

Index of poems by first line